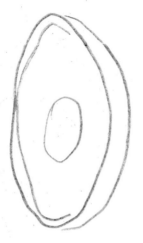

GRAPHIC SCIENCE

THE **SHOCKING WORLD** OF

# ELECTRICITY

WITH **MAX AXIOM**
SUPER SCIENTIST

Liam O'Donnell
illustrated by Richard Dominguez
and Charles Barnett

www.raintreepublishers.co.uk
Visit our website to find out
more information about
Raintree books.

**To order:**

☎ Phone +44 (0) 1865 888066

🖷 Fax +44 (0) 1865 314091

🖳 Visit www.raintreepublishers.co.uk

Raintree is an imprint of Capstone Global Library Limited, a company incorporated in England and
Wales having its registered office at 7 Pilgrim Street, London EC4V 6LB
Registered company number: 6695882

"Raintree" is a registered trademark of Pearson Education Limited, under licence to Capstone Global
Library Limited

ISBN 978 1 4062 1453 6 (hardback)
14 13 12 11 10

**British Library Cataloguing in Publication Data**
O'Donnell, Liam, 1970-
Electricity. -- (Graphic science)
537-dc22
A full catalogue record for this book is available from the British Library.

Art Director and Designer: Bob Lentz
Cover Artist: Tod Smith
Colourists: Ben Huneker and Kim Brown
UK Editor: Harriet Milles
UK Production: Alison Parsons
Originated by Capstone Global Library
Printed and bound in China by South China Printing Company Limited

**Disclaimer**
All the Internet addresses (URLs) given in this book were valid at the time of going to press.
However, due to the dynamic nature of the Internet, some addresses may have changed, or sites may
have changed or ceased to exist since publication. While the publisher regrets any inconvenience this
may cause reade                              ibility for any such changes can be accepted by the publisher.

# CONTENTS

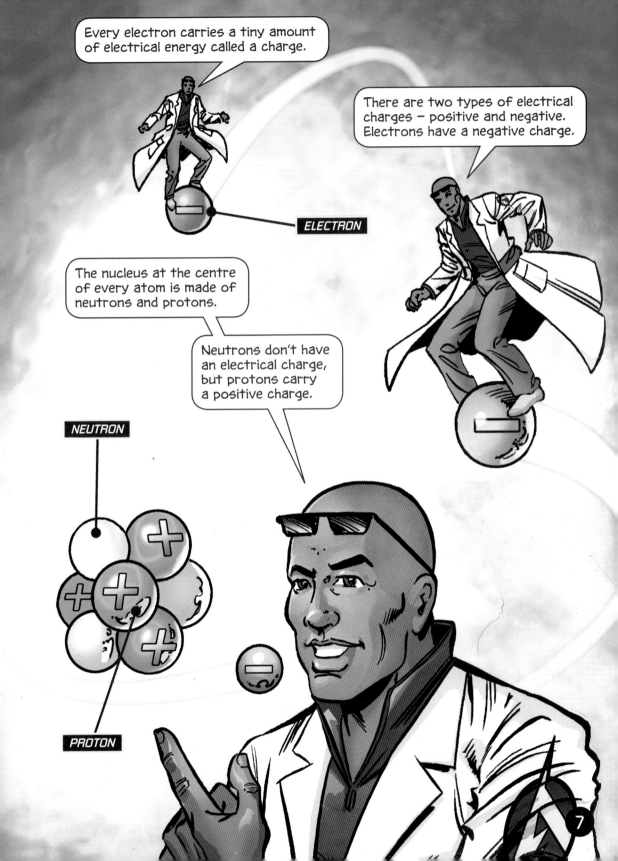

TURBINE: Steam from boiling water turns the blades on this machine.

MAGNET: The turbine spins a giant magnet, causing electrons to jump from their atoms.

MAX AXIOM

SUBJECT: POWER STATION GENERATOR

WIRE COIL: Jumping electrons are captured and pushed along a coiled wire.

ELECTRIC FLOW: The charged electrons flow out of the generator as electricity.

Thanks for the tour, Denise. I'm heading up to the roof to see where the electricity is going next.

Any time, Max! Take this walkie-talkie, and give me a call if you need anything else.

Wind turbines create power in much the same way. Instead of steam, blowing wind turns the turbine.

Fast-moving water can turn turbines as well.

Once the electricity is created, it has to travel from the generator to our homes.

That's why we've come to the roof.

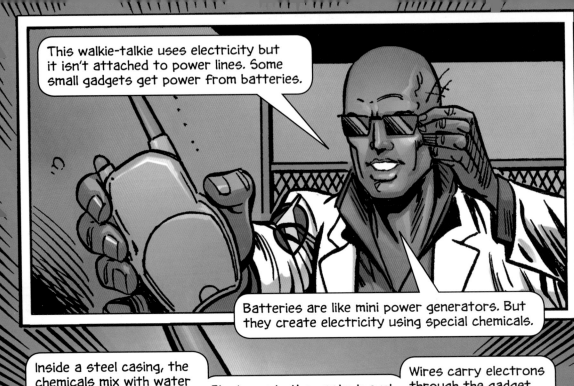

This walkie-talkie uses electricity but it isn't attached to power lines. Some small gadgets get power from batteries.

Batteries are like mini power generators. But they create electricity using special chemicals.

Inside a steel casing, the chemicals mix with water and zinc to form a paste.

Electrons in the paste travel out of the battery through a brass pin called a collector.

Wires carry electrons through the gadget as electricity.

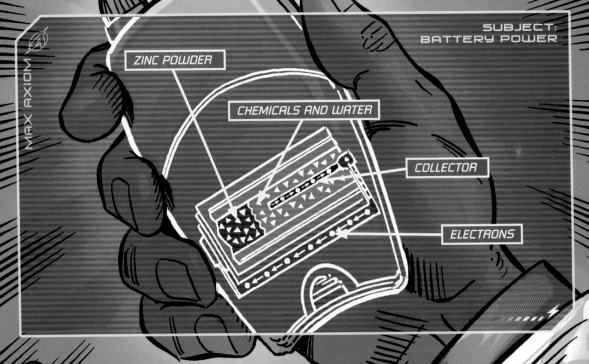

SUBJECT:
BATTERY POWER

MAX AXIOM

ZINC POWDER

CHEMICALS AND WATER

COLLECTOR

ELECTRONS

# MORE ABOUT ELECTRICITY

In 1752, inventor Benjamin Franklin flew a kite during a thunderstorm to prove that lightning is electricity. As his kite entered a darkened cloud, electricity surged down the string to a key that Franklin had attached to the end. When Franklin touched the key, he got a shock. This painful experiment convinced Franklin that lightning and electricity were the same.

In fact, lightning is an extreme form of static electricity. Inside storm clouds, small particles rub together to create a negative electrical charge. This negative electricity stretches down towards positive electricity, which begins rising from the ground. The opposite charges meet to form a brilliant bolt of lightning.

On October 21, 1879, inventor Thomas Edison created an incandescent light bulb. Nearly three years later, he opened the first central power station in New York City. Soon, thousands of Americans were lighting their homes with Edison's bulbs.

Storms are filled with natural electricity, but sunny skies have energy as well. Solar power is a renewable source of energy from the sun. Specially designed panels capture sunlight and turn it into electricity.

The cables that carry electricity to our homes are extremely dangerous. So, how do birds perch safely on top of them? Electricity always looks for the closest path to the ground. Since birds aren't touching the ground, electricity continues safely along the wires. However, if a person touches the wires while in contact with the ground, he or she could receive a deadly electric shock.

Electricity can also be generated through nuclear fusion. During this process, atoms are smashed together to create an extra electron. The electron creates energy to boil water and turn a turbine. Like solar power, nuclear energy doesn't pollute the air. Unfortunately, it creates dangerous waste.

 Creating electricity often creates pollution, which can be harmful to the environment. To help reduce the amount of electricity used in your home, replace incandescent light bulbs with fluorescent ones. They can last almost 13 times longer and save electricity.

## MORE ABOUT

SUPER SCIENTIST

Real Name: Maxwell Axiom
Height: 1.86 m (6 ft. 1 in.)
Weight: 87 kg (13 st. 10 lb.)
Eyes: Brown   Hair: None

Super capabilities: Super intelligence; able to shrink to the size of an atom; sunglasses give X-ray vision; lab coat allows for travel through time and space.

Origin: Since birth, Max Axiom seemed destined for greatness. His mother, a marine biologist, taught her son about the mysteries of the sea. His father, a nuclear physicist and volunteer park warden, showed Max the wonders of the earth and sky.

One day, while Max was hiking in the hills, a megacharged lightning bolt struck him with blinding fury. When he awoke, he discovered a new-found energy and set out to learn as much about science as possible. He travelled the globe studying every aspect of the subject. Then he was ready to share his knowledge and new identity with  the world. He had become Max Axiom, Super Scientist.

# GLOSSARY

**amp** unit used to measure the strength of an electrical current

**circuit** path for electricity to flow through

**conductor** material that lets electricity travel easily through it

**current** flow of electrical charge

**electron** tiny particle in an atom that travels around the nucleus

**energy** ability to move things or do work

**generator** machine that makes electricity by turning a magnet inside a coil of wire

**insulator** material that blocks an electric current

**nucleus** centre of an atom, made up of neutrons and protons

**proton** one of the very small parts in an atom's nucleus

**turbine** engine with a fan-like device that is turned by steam, wind, or gas

**watt** unit for measuring electrical power

# FIND OUT MORE

## Books

*Electricity and Magnetism*, Peter Adamczyk and Paul Francis Law (Usborne, 2008)

*Electrical Experiments* (Do It Yourself series), Rachel Lynette (Heinemann Library, 2008)

*Thomas Edison*, Jan Adkins (DK Publishing, 2009)

## Websites

http://www.switchedonkids.org.uk/index.html
This site gives a basic explanation about where electricity comes from.

http://sciencemuseum.org.uk/On-line/energy/site/quiz2.asp
Try the quiz and find out more information about electricity along the way.

# INDEX